The Hu

written and illustrated by Diane-Elizabeth Napier

Copyright © 2004 Ransom Publishing Ltd.
ISBN: 1 84167 182 7
Printed and bound at Ajanta Offset, New Delhi, India.
The right of Diane-Elizabeth Napier to be identified as author of this Work
has been asserted by her in accordance with sections 77 and 78
of the Copyright, Designs and Patents Act 1988.

Ransom Publishing Ltd.
Rose Cottage
Howe Hill
Watlington
Oxfordshire
OX49 5HB
UK

www.ransom.co.uk

Up here, on there,
Under, over, everywhere!

Bobby looked
for his little cup.

He looked up here,
He looked on there,
Under, over, everywhere.

But the fun had just begun!

Was it here? Was it there?
Was it ... was it anywhere?

He hunted here,
he hunted there.
He hunted and hunted for it
everywhere.

In the end, Bobby said:
"I give up!"
"OK," said Copy Cat.
"Here's your cup."

Then Bobby said:
"Give me the cup. Let me
play too."

"You hunt the cup.
It's a problem for you."

Andy looked, and then he said: "Having a spaceship is not just for fun."

"We are MUCH too near
the Sun!
If our spaceship
gets too near ..."

"… it will melt.
Oh dear! Oh dear!"

U u   The Hunt

Up here, on there,
Under, over, everywhere!
Bobby looked for his little cup.
He looked up here,
He looked on there,
Under, over, everywhere.

But the fun had just begun!
Was it here? Was it there?
Was it ... was it anywhere?

He hunted here, he hunted there.
He hunted and hunted for it everywhere.
In the end, Bobby said: "I give up!"
"OK," said Copy Cat.
"Here's your cup."

Then Bobby said:
"Give me the cup. Let me play too.
You hunt the cup. It's a problem for you."
Andy looked, and then he said:
"Having a spaceship is not just for
fun. We are MUCH too near the Sun!
If our spaceship gets too near …
… it will melt. Oh dear! Oh dear!"

Fifteen New Words

hunt

Page 2   under

Page 3   cup

Page 5   begun

Page 6   anywhere

Page 7   hunted

Page 8   give
OK
Here's

Page 10   problem

Page 11   having

Page 12   near
our

Page 13   melt
dear

Uu

Spellings to Learn:

1. up
2. cup
3. run
4. sun
5. fun
6. Mum
7. us
8. fuss
9. under
10. unhappy

Handwriting Practice:
copy these

Uu   Uu   Uu

Phonic Practice

Can you sound out these words?

ar

far

car

jar

star

hard

start

Uu
Alphabetical Useful Word List

ugly

umbrella

uncle
under

unhappy
unhelpful

uniform
unit
universe

unless
until
unzipped

up
use

The Alphabet

Aa Bb Cc Dd Ee

Ff Gg Hh Ii Jj

Kk Ll Mm Nn Oo

Pp Qq Rr Ss Tt

Uu Vv Ww Xx Yy

Zz